Initial

V   S

CW00408664

Wakefield Music Services

COLLEGE LONDON

THE EXAM AT A GLANCE

For your Rock & Pop exam you will need to perform a set of **three songs** and one of the **Session skills** assessments, either **Playback** or **Improvising**. You can choose the order in which you perform your set-list.

Song 1

Choose a song from this book

OR from www.trinityrock.com/downloads.

Song 2

Choose a different song from this book

OR from www.trinityrock.com/downloads

OR perform a song you have chosen yourself: this could be your own cover version or a song you have written. It should be at the same level as the songs in this book.

Song 3: Technical focus

Choose one of the Technical focus songs from this book, which cover three specific technical elements.

Session skills

Choose either **Playback** or **Improvising**.

When you are preparing for your exam please check on **www.trinityrock.com** for the most up-to-date information and requirements as these can change from time to time.

CONTENTS

Trinity College London's Rock & Pop syllabus and supporting publications
have been devised and produced in association with
Faber Music and Peters Edition London.

Trinity College London
Registered office:
89 Albert Embankment
London SE1 7TP UK
T + 44 (0)20 7820 6100
F + 44 (0)20 7820 6161
E music@trinitycollege.co.uk
www.trinitycollege.co.uk

Registered in the UK. Company no. 02683033
Charity no. 1014792
Patron HRH The Duke of Kent KG

Copyright © 2012 Trinity College London
First published in 2012 by Trinity College London

Cover and book design by Chloë Alexander
Brand development by Andy Ashburner @ Caffeinehit (www.caffeinehit.com)
Photographs courtesy of Rex Features Limited.
Printed in England by Caligraving Ltd

Audio produced, mixed & mastered by Tom Fleming
Vocal arrangements by Oliver Weeks
Backing tracks arranged by Tom Fleming
Vocal Consultant: Heidi Pegler

Musicians
Vocals: Bo Walton, Brendan Reilly & Alison Symons
Keyboards: Oliver Weeks
Guitar & Bass: Tom Fleming
Bass: Ben Hillyard
Drums: George Double
Studio Engineer: Joel Davies www.thelimehouse.com

ISBN: 978-0-85736-254-4

SONGS

SEASONS IN THE SUN

Terry Jacks
English Words by Rod McKuen • Music by Jacques Brel

♩ = 88 **Steady Ballad**

1.Good-bye to you my trust-ed friend,

we've known each o-ther since we were nine or ten,— to-ge-ther we've climbed hills and

trees, learned of love and A B Cs, skinned our hearts and skinned our

Alternative higher key available from www.trinityrock.com

SONGS GREAT DJ

Ting Tings
Words and Music by Julian De Martino and Katie White

Alternative higher key available from www.trinityrock.com

NEW YORK MINING DISASTER 1941

Bee Gees

Words and Music by Barry Gibb and Robin Gibb

In the e- vent of some-thing hap- pen- ing to

me, there is some-thing I would like you all to see. It's just a

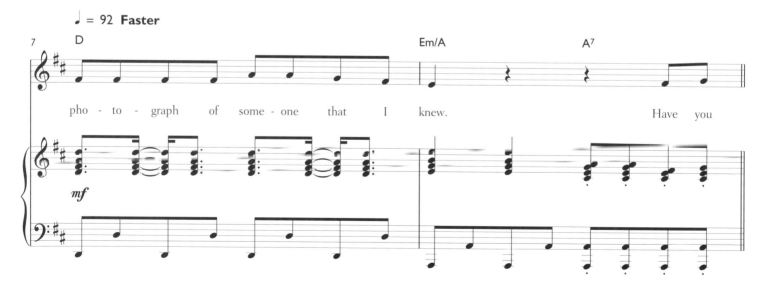

pho- to- graph of some- one that I knew. Have you

Alternative lower key available from www.trinityrock.com

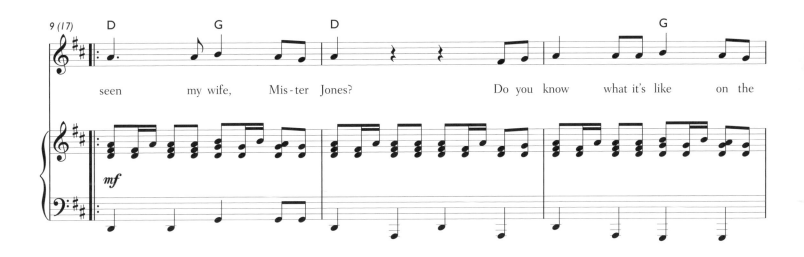

seen my wife, Mis-ter Jones? Do you know what it's like on the

out - side? Don't go talk - ing too loud, you'll cause

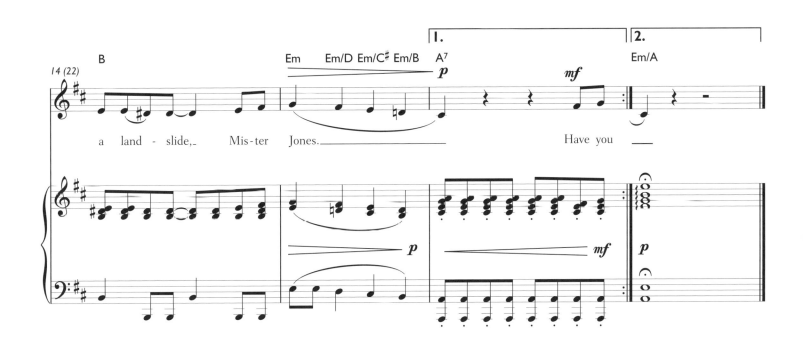

a land - slide,_ Mis-ter Jones._____ Have you ____

SONGS | BLACK BETTY

Lead Belly
New Words and New Music Arrangement by Huddie Ledbetter

♩ = 88 **Blues Rock**

YOUR PAGE NOTES

I AM THE MUSIC MAN

In your exam, you will be assessed on the following elements:

1 Counting rests

'I Am The Music Man' has a two bar intro before the vocals come in. You will need to count: **1** 2 3 4 **1** 2 3 4.

The vocals do not start on the first beat of the bar but on the final ♪ – this is usually known as a 'pick up' in rock and pop music. It is also sometimes called an upbeat or *anacrusis*. You need to count carefully so that you come in exactly at the right place.

You also need to count carefully in bars 5–6 to make sure that your entries are right on time.

2 Pitching the notes

An interval is the distance in pitch between any two notes. Most of the intervals in 'I Am The Music Man' are quite small: these are relatively easy to pitch. The end of the first phrase has a rising note on the word 'man'. Watch out for this.

Make sure you pitch the B in bar 6 (on 'I play piano') correctly. It is lower than the previous phrase, which starts on a D.

3 Slurs

There are slurs ⌒ at the beginning of bars 5, 6 and 7 (and later in the song). Sing them as smoothly as you can.

TECHNICAL FOCUS SONGS

BAND OPTION

I AM THE MUSIC MAN

Black Lace
Trad

www.trinityrock.com

YOUR PAGE NOTES

DA DOO RON RON

In your exam, you will be assessed on the following technical elements:

1 Breathing

'Da Doo Ron Ron' is marked f, which stands for *forte* and means sing loudly.
To help you sing loudly, take a breath in between each phrase on the first page:

I met him on a Monday and my heart stood still (*breath*)
Da doo ron ron ron, da doo ron, ron (*breath*)
Somebody told me that his name was Bill (*breath*)
Da doo ron ron ron, da doo ron, ron (*breath*)

Each time you sing 'yes' it should be joyful and exuberant but without being shouted. Take a quick breath before the final ♪ in bar 19 so you can hold the last note for its full length.

2 Swung ♪

The instruction at the top of the page says 'Swung'. This means that when you come to the ♪ notes you should put a little more emphasis on the first of each pair, making it slightly longer.

3 Counting rests

'Da Doo Ron Ron' has a four-bar intro before the vocals come in. You will need to count **1** 2 3 4 **1** 2 3 4 **1** 2 3 4 **1** 2 3 4.

The vocals do not start on the first beat of the bar but on the final ♪ – this is usually known as a 'pick up' in rock and pop music. It is also sometimes called an upbeat or *anacrusis*. You will need to count so that you come in at exactly the right place.

DA DOO RON RON

The Crystals
Words and Music by Ellie Greenwich, Jeff Barry and Phil Spector

Alternative lower key available from www.trinityrock.com

ABOUT THE SONGS

SEASONS IN THE SUN

Terry Jacks

'Seasons In The Sun' is a version of 'Le Moribond', a song by Belgian singer-songwriter Jacques Brel, with new lyrics by the American poet and singer Rod McKuen. The Canadian singer Terry Jacks had been invited to make a recording of 'Seasons In The Sun' with The Beach Boys. The band abandoned the project, but Jacks recorded the song nonetheless.

'Seasons In The Sun' was recorded in Vancouver in 1974 and soon became a worldwide hit. Since then there have been many versions made by, among others, The Beach Boys, Nirvana, and Westlife.

PERFORMANCE · HINTS & TIPS ·

The first three vocal entries come in on a half-beat. If you find this tricky to feel, try clapping or stamping on the first beat of the bar and then singing immediately after.

In bar 11, you need a really quick breath after the word 'knees' to make sure that you start the next phrase on time.

The final chorus should be loud and anthem-like. Try singing the final line in one breath.

Remember that if this key doesn't suit your voice there is an alternative version available from www.trinityrock.com in a higher key.

'Together we've climbed hills and trees'

GREAT DJ

Ting Tings

The Ting Tings are a dance-oriented indie pop duo made up of singer and guitarist Katie White and drummer Jules De Martino. The band was formed in Salford in 2006 where the two lived in an artists' collective. Their first double-A-side single 'That's Not My Name/Great DJ' was first released by the band on a local label – Switchflicker Records. The song was later re-released by Columbia on the album *We Started Nothing*.

When Katie White wrote 'Great DJ' she could only play one chord on the guitar. By accidentally putting her finger on the wrong string, she discovered another chord. The two chords formed the basis of the song's riff.

There are several accidentals in this song. An accidental is a sharp (♯), flat (♭) or natural (♮) used during the song but not part of the key signature. 'Great DJ' is in the key of D and so the key signature has two sharps – F♯ and C♯. But some notes have accidentals: watch out for the F♮s near the end of this song.

Accidental signs last for the whole bar. So, in bar 25, all the Fs are F♮s.

You have to sing 'the drums' twelve times in a row at the end of the song, so you will need to count them.

Remember that if this key doesn't suit your voice there is an alternative version available from www.trinityrock.com in a higher key.

'Swallow *worries* one *by* one'

NEW YORK MINING DISASTER 1941

Bee Gees

The Bee Gees was originally formed by three brothers, Barry (vocals and guitar), Robin (vocals) and Maurice Gibb (vocals and bass); they were later joined by a drummer and a guitarist.

The Bee Gees co-wrote all of their songs. They had a distinctive sound, combining high-pitched voices with striking harmonies. The band reinvented themselves from a successful pop act of the late 1960s/early 1970s to a leading group during the disco music era of the late 1970s. It has been estimated that their total record sales are over 220 million.

'New York Mining Disaster 1941' was a 1967 hit for the Bee Gees and the first record they released in the USA. This haunting song tells the story of a miner trapped underground. He is showing a photo of his wife to a work-mate while they wait to be rescued.

PERFORMANCE · HINTS & TIPS

'New York Mining Disaster 1941' is marked *p* at the beginning of the song. This stands for *piano* and means that you should sing quietly. There is a different dynamic marking for the second section of the song – *mf* . This stands for *mezzo forte* and means that you should sing moderately loudly.

Look out for the tie: ⌣ in bar 14, on the word 'slide'. Think of the two tied notes as one, lasting the length of the two notes added together.

The ▱ symbol in bar 15 is a *diminuendo* sign. It means that you should get gradually quieter.

Remember that if this key doesn't suit your voice there is an alternative version available from www.trinityrock.com in a lower key.

'Do you *know* what it's *like* on *the* outside?'

BLACK BETTY

Lead Belly

'Black Betty' is an African-American worksong (an early type of black American music sung rhythmically while doing manual labour). Nobody really knows who Black Betty was, but many believe that the name was slang for a prison bullwhip or a bottle of whisky.

'Black Betty' is normally credited to Lead Belly, although he was not the first to record it. Born Huddie Ledbetter, Lead Belly was a wandering musician who spent more than one spell in prison, including a long stretch for murder. His talent as a folk-blues singer and 12-string guitarist was recognised by the folk-music researcher and collector John Lomax, who later secured his release from prison (although he was soon back inside for assault).

Lead Belly's songs have been recorded by Pete Seeger, Lonnie Donegan, The Fall and Nick Cave. The most famous recording of 'Black Betty' was by Ram Jam – it was their only hit.

The words and rhythm are very precise in 'Black Betty' and need to be crisp and clear throughout. It is quite a repetitive song so needs a strong drive to keep it moving forward.

The song opens with straight ♩ beats on the bass drum. This helps you keep a steady beat. Listen out for the ♪ beat in the guitar part – this will help keep you in time and make your entries accurate.

The 't' in 'Betty' should be quite dry – almost like a 'd'.

'Oh *she* make me *sing*'

I AM THE MUSIC MAN

Trad.

The origins of 'I Am The Music Man' are uncertain. It is usually sung as an action song where the singers act out playing the different instruments and sometimes imitate the sound of the instruments as well. In 1990 it was recorded by the British pop group Black Lace.

PERFORMANCE · HINTS & TIPS ·

This is a jolly song so let it bounce along quite loudly and with a strong beat all the way through.

Most of the song is marked mf. This stands for *mezzo forte* and means that you should sing moderately loudly. At bar 16, the dynamic changes to mp. This stands for *mezzo piano* and means that you should sing moderately quietly. Make sure that there is a difference between mf and mp.

The vocalist does not sing the final phrase, but leaves the last 'yes I can play' hanging.

'I can *play* *yes* I *can* play'

DA DOO RON RON

The Crystals

The late 1950s saw the rise of 'girl groups' such as The Shangri-Las, The Crystals and The Shirelles. Their music was characterised by a high-pitched teen girl sound and doo wop based vocal harmonies, often with a backing of strings and dramatic drumbeats. The lyrics were about relationships and the search for love – something with which teenagers always identify.

The 1963 hit single 'Da Doo Ron Ron' was written by the songwriters Ellie Greenwich and Jeff Barry who, along with many other songwriters, worked in the famous Brill Building – a New York 'hit factory' of the time. It was produced by Phil Spector who was famous for his 'Wall of Sound' – the unique dense texture he achieved through combining layers of large groups of instruments and imaginative echo-laden sound engineering.

Listen out for the backing vocals on the words 'Da Doo Ron Ron Ron' and make sure that you are rhythmically together and in tune with them.

The rhythm at the start of the second phrase ('somebody told me . . .') might need some practice. Sing this phrase several times until it feels comfortable and sounds entirely natural.

Remember that if this key doesn't suit your voice there is an alternative version available from www.trinityrock.com in a lower key.

PERFORMANCE · HINTS & TIPS ·

'And when he *walked me* home'

PLAYBACK

For your exam, you can choose either Playback or Improvising (see page 27). If you choose Playback, you will be asked to sing some music you have not seen or heard before.

In the exam, you will be given the song chart and the examiner will play a recording of the music on a CD. You will hear several two-bar phrases on the CD: you should sing each of them straight back in turn. There's a rhythm track going throughout, which helps you keep in time. There should not be any gaps in the music.

In the exam you will have two chances to sing with the CD:
- First time – for practice
- Second time – for assessment.

You should listen to the audio, copying what you hear; you can also read the music. Here are some practice song charts – which are also on the CD in this book. The music is printed without text and may be sung to any vowels (with or without consonants), or to sol-fa.

Practice playback 1

Practice playback 2

SESSION SKILLS

IMPROVISING

For your exam, you can choose either Playback (see page 26), or Improvising.
If you choose to improvise, you will be asked to improvise over a backing track that
you haven't heard before in a specified style.

In the exam, you will be given a song chart and the examiner will play a recording of
the backing track on CD. The backing track consists of a passage of music played on
a loop. You should improvise a melody line over it.

In the exam you will have two chances to perform with the CD:
* First time – for practice
* Second time – for assessment.

Here are some practice improvisation charts which are also on the CD in this book.
The music is printed without text and may be sung to any vowels (with or without
consonants), or to sol-fa.

Practice improvisation 1

♩ = 120 **Pop**

C   G   C   G

Practice improvisation 2

♩ = 110 **Pop**

E   A   E   E

CHOOSING A SONG FOR YOUR EXAM

There are lots of options to help you choose your three songs for the exam.
For Songs 1 and 2, you can choose a song which is:

- from this book
- from www.trinityrock.com/downloads

Or for Song 2 you can choose a song which is:

- sheet music from a printed or online source.
- your own arrangement of a song or a song you have written yourself (see page 29).

You can perform the song unaccompanied or with a backing track (minus the solo voice). If you like, you can create a backing track yourself (or with friends).

For Initial, the song should be between 30 seconds and two minutes long, and the level of difficulty should be similar to your other songs.
When choosing a song, think about:

- Does it work for my voice?
- Are there any technical elements that are too difficult for me? (If so, perhaps save it for when you do the next grade.)
- Do I enjoy singing it?
- Does it work with my other songs to create a good set-list?

SHEET MUSIC

You must always bring an original copy of the book or a download sheet with email certificate for each song you perform in the exam. If you choose to write your own song you must provide the examiner with a copy of the sheet music.
Your music can be:

- a lead sheet with lyrics, chords and melody line
- a chord chart with lyrics
- a full score using conventional staff notation
- see page 29 for details on presenting a song you have written yourself

The title of the song and your name should be on the sheet music.

HELP PAGES

WRITING YOUR OWN SONG

You can perform a song that you have written yourself for one of the choices in your exam. For Initial, your song should last between 30 seconds and two minutes, so it is likely to be quite straightforward. It is sometimes difficult to know where to begin, however. Here are some suggestions for starting points:

- **A melody**: many songs are made up around a 'hook' (a short catchy melodic idea, usually only a few notes long).
Try writing a couple of ideas for hooks here:

- **A chord sequence**: a short chord sequence can provide an entire verse or chorus. Write your ideas for a chord sequence here:

- **A rhythm**: a short repeated rhythm will often underpin an entire song.
Think of a couple of short rhythms you could use here:

There are plenty of other ways of starting: perhaps with a riff or a lyric, for example.

You will also need to consider the **structure** of your song (verse and chorus, 12-bar blues, and so on), the **style** it is in (blues, hard rock, etc.), and what **instruments** it is for (solo voice or voice/keyboards/drums . . .).

There are many choices to be made – which is why writing a song is such a rewarding thing to do.

WRITING YOUR SONG DOWN

Rock and pop music is often written as a **lead sheet** with the lyrics (if there are any), chords and a melody line.

You can, if you prefer, use a **graph** or **table** to represent your music, as long as it is clear to anyone else (including the examiner) how the song goes.

SINGING IN A BAND

Singing in a band is exciting: it can be a lot of fun and, as with everything, the more you do it, the easier it gets. It is very different from singing on your own. Everyone contributes to the overall sound: the most important skill you need to develop is listening.

For a band to sound good, the musicians need to be 'together' – that mainly means keeping in time with each other, but also performing at the same volume, and with the same kind of feeling.

Your relationship with the other band members is also important. Talk with them about the music you perform, the music you like, and what you'd like the band to achieve short-term and long-term.

Band rehearsals are important – you should not be late, tired or distracted by your mobile phone! Being positive makes a huge difference. Try to create a friendly atmosphere in rehearsals so that everybody feels comfortable trying out new things. Don't worry about making mistakes: that is what rehearsals are for.

'Black Betty' (page 10) and 'I Am The Music Man' (page 14) are arranged for band. You will find parts for keyboards, guitar, bass and drums in the other Trinity Rock & Pop Initial books or available online. Trinity offers exams for groups of musicians at various levels. The songs arranged for bands are ideal to include as part of a set-list for these exams. Have a look at the website for more details.

HINTS AND TIPS

- When you are starting out, it is easier if you have only one of each instrument, so that you can hear clearly what everybody is playing.

- Record your practice sessions and listen back for sections that worked well and bits that had problems.

- Meet up regularly to socialise before and after rehearsals to help keep in touch with each other.

PERFORMING WITH BACKING TRACKS

The CD contains demos and backing tracks of all the songs in the book.
The additional songs at www.trinityrock.com/downloads also come with demos and backing tracks

- In your exam, you should perform with the backing track, or you can create your own (see below).
- The backing tracks begin with a click track, which sets the tempo and helps you start accurately.
- Be careful to balance the volume of the backing track against your voice.
- Listen carefully to the backing track to ensure you are singing in time.

If you are creating your own backing track here are some further tips:
- Make sure the sound quality is of a good standard.
- Think carefully about the instruments/sounds you are putting on the backing track.
- Avoid copying what you are singing on the backing track – it should support not duplicate.
- Do you need to include a click track at the beginning?

COPYRIGHT IN A SONG

If you are a singer or songwriter it is important to know about copyright. When someone writes a song or creates an arrangement they own the copyright (sometimes called 'the rights') to that version. The copyright means that other people cannot copy it, sell it, perform it in a concert, make it available online or record it without the owner's permission or the appropriate licence. When you write a song you automatically own the copyright to it, which means that other people cannot copy your work. But, just as importantly, you cannot copy other people's work, or perform it in public without their permission or the appropriate licence.

Points to remember

- You can create a cover version of a song and play in it in an exam or other non-public performance.
- You cannot record your cover version and make your recording available to others (by copying it or uploading it to a website) without the appropriate licence.
- You do own the copyright of your own original song, which means that no one is allowed to copy it.
- You cannot copy someone else's song without their permission or the appropriate licence.

ALSO AVAILABLE

Trinity College London Rock & Pop examinations 2012-2017 are also available for:

Bass Initial
ISBN: 978-0-85736-227-8

Bass Grade 1
ISBN: 978-0-85736-228-5

Bass Grade 2
ISBN: 978-0-85736-229-2

Bass Grade 3
ISBN: 978-0-85736-230-8

Bass Grade 4
ISBN: 978-0-85736-231-5

Bass Grade 5
ISBN: 978-0-85736-232-2

Bass Grade 6
ISBN: 978-0-85736-233-9

Bass Grade 7
ISBN: 978-0-85736-234-6

Bass Grade 8
ISBN: 978-0-85736-235-3

Drums Initial
ISBN: 978-0-85736-245-2

Drums Grade 1
ISBN: 978-0-85736-246-9

Drums Grade 2
ISBN: 978-0-85736-247-6

Drums Grade 3
ISBN: 978-0-85736-248-3

Drums Grade 4
ISBN: 978-0-85736-249-0

Drums Grade 5
ISBN: 978-0-85736-250-6

Drums Grade 6
ISBN: 978-0-85736-251-3

Drums Grade 7
ISBN: 978-0-85736-252-0

Drums Grade 8
ISBN: 978-0-85736-253-7

Guitar Initial
ISBN: 978-0-85736-218-6

Guitar Grade 1
ISBN: 978-0-85736-219-3

Guitar Grade 2
ISBN: 978-0-85736-220-9

Guitar Grade 3
ISBN: 978-0-85736-221-6

Guitar Grade 4
IODN: 970-0-05730-222-3

Guitar Grade 5
ISBN: 978-0-85736-223-0

Guitar Grade 6
ISBN: 978-0-85736-224-7

Guitar Grade 7
ISBN: 978-0-85736-225-4

Guitar Grade 8
ISBN: 978-0-85736-226-1

Keyboards Initial
ISBN: 978-0-85736-236-0

Keyboards Grade 1
ISBN: 978-0-85736-237-7

Keyboards Grade 2
ISBN: 978-0-85736-238-4

Keyboards Grade 3
ISBN: 978-0-85736-239-1

Keyboards Grade 4
ISBN: 978-0-85736-240-7

Keyboards Grade 5
ISBN: 978-0-85736-241-4

Keyboards Grade 6
ISBN: 978-0-85736-242-1

Keyboards Grade 7
ISBN: 978-0-85736-243-8

Keyboards Grade 8
ISBN: 978-0-85736-244-5

Vocals Initial
ISBN: 978-0-85736-254-4

Vocals Grade 1
ISBN: 978-0-85736-255-1

Vocals Grade 2
ISBN: 978-0-85736-256-8

Vocals Grade 3
ISBN: 978-0-85736-257-5

Vocals Grade 4
ISBN: 978-0-85736-258-2

Vocals Grade 5
ISBN: 978-0-85736-259-9

Vocals Grade 6 (female voice)
ISBN: 978-0-85736-263-6

Vocals Grade 6 (male voice)
ISBN: 978-0-85736-260-5

Vocals Grade 7 (female voice)
ISBN: 978-0-85736-264-3

Vocals Grade 7 (male voice)
ISBN: 978-0-85736-261-2

Vocals Grade 8 (female voice)
ISBN: 978-0-85736-265-0

Vocals Grade 8 (male voice)
ISBN: 978-0-85736-262-9